Music for Piano

Pachelbel's Canon

Arranged by Colin Hand

CANON IN D

Johann Pachelbel (1653 - 1706)
arranged Colin Hand

3

4

coll'8 ad lib.

poco rit.

Allargando

ff

molto rit.

6

We hope you enjoy the music in this book.
Further copies of this and our many other books are available
from your local music shop or Christian bookshop.

In case of difficulty, please contact the publisher direct by writing to:

The Sales Department
KEVIN MAYHEW LTD
Buxhall
Stowmarket
Suffolk IP14 3BW

Phone 01449 737978
Fax 01449 737834

Please ask for our complete catalogue of outstanding Instrumental Music.

Cover designed by Jonathan Stroulger

First published in Great Britain in 1995 by Kevin Mayhew Ltd

© Copyright 1995 Kevin Mayhew Ltd

ISBN 0 86209 712 6
Catalogue No: 3611170

8 9

Music Editor: Tamzin Howard
Music setting by Tracy Cracknell

Printed and bound in Great Britain